1 Separate the words in the word snakes and then write them out next to the correct pictures.

a lesinfos **b** lessériespolicières **c** lesjeuxtélévisés **d** lesdocumentaires **e** lesémissionsdetélé-réalité le- isdesport

 1 _____

 **2** _____

_____

 3 _____

 4 _____

 5 _____

 6 Le Journal  _____

2 Are the phrases positive or negative? Write them in the correct column.

Positive 👍	Negative 👎
	C'est nul.

C'est nul.
C'est génial.
C'est intéressant.
Je n'aime pas ça.
C'est barbant.
J'aime ça.
C'est amusant.
C'est ennuyeux.

3 Complete these texts with the correct French word or phrase from exercise 2.

1 **Hugo**
Moi, je regarde les documentaires. _____ (I like them.)
Mais les émissions de sport, _____ . (I don't like them.)

2 **Manon**
Je regarde les émissions de télé-réalité,
c'est _____ . (interesting)
J'aime aussi les séries policières, c'est _____ ! (funny)

3 **Théo**
Moi, je regarde les émissions de sport.
C'est _____ . (great)
Je n'aime pas les infos. C'est _____ . (boring)

J'ai une passion pour le cinéma
(pages 10–11)

1 Complete the puzzle with the correct types of film.
Use the words in the box below.

```
                                    1
                                    c
                        2           o
                        3           m
                    4               é
            5                       d
                    6               i
            7                       e
                        8           s
```

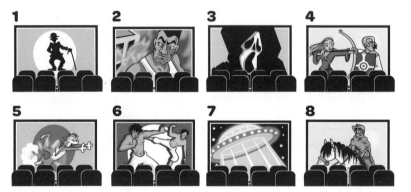

> westerns
> films fantastiques
> comédies
> films d'horreur
> dessins animés
> films d'arts martiaux
> films de science-fiction
> films d'action

2 Write the appropriate answer (a–d) after each question.

1 Qu'est-ce que tu aimes comme films?

_____

2 Qu'est-ce que tu n'aimes pas?

_____

3 Quel est ton film préféré?

_____

4 Qui est ton acteur préféré?

_____

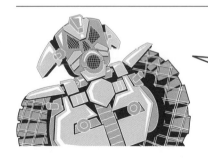

> **a** Mon film préféré, c'est *Transformers*.
> **b** Mon acteur préféré, c'est Shia LaBeouf.
> **c** Je n'aime pas les comédies.
> **d** J'aime les films d'action.

3 Adapt the underlined parts to write your own answers to questions 1–4.

1 **Crack the code for the missing vowels and write out the sentences.**

a = _@_   e = _____   i = _____   o = _____   u = _____

1 J% l#s ?n r*m@n p*l#c#%r.   _____

2 J% l#s ?n l#vr% d'%p*?v@nt%.   _____

3 J% l#s ?n m@g@z#n% s?r l%s c%́l%́br#t%́s.   _____

4 J% l#s ?n r*m@n f@nt@st#q?%.   _____

5 J% l#s ?n% BD.   _____

6 J% l#s ?n l#vr% s?r l%s @n#m@?x.   _____

2 **Write a sentence about each picture. Choose one item from each column.**

1    **2**    **3**

4    **5**    **6**

Je lis une BD.	C'est assez bien.
Je lis un magazine sur les célébrités.	C'est amusant.
Je lis un livre d'épouvante.	~~C'est intéressant.~~
~~Je lis un roman policier.~~	C'est nul.
Je lis un livre sur les animaux.	C'est passionnant.
Je lis un roman fantastique.	C'est ennuyeux.

1 Je lis *un roman policier*. C'est intéressant. _____

2 _____

3 _____

4 _____

5 _____

6 _____

3 **Change one item in each sentence to say something different.**

Je lis *une BD*. C'est intéressant. _____

1 **Do the quiz! Choose the best answers for you.**

Tu es accro à Internet?

1 Je fais des achats en ligne:
- ◆ tous les soirs ☐
- ■ souvent ☐
- ▲ quelquefois ☐

4 Je fais des recherches pour mes devoirs:
- ◆ tous les soirs ☐
- ■ souvent ☐
- ▲ quelquefois ☐

2 Je lis des blogs:
- ◆ d'habitude ☐
- ■ une fois par semaine ☐
- ▲ quelquefois ☐

5 J'envoie des e-mails:
- ◆ tous les jours ☐
- ■ une fois par semaine ☐
- ▲ quelquefois ☐

3 Je joue à des jeux en ligne:
- ◆ tous les jours ☐
- ■ deux fois par semaine ☐
- ▲ quelquefois ☐

6 Je fais des quiz:
- ◆ souvent ☐
- ■ une fois par semaine ☐
- ▲ quelquefois ☐

> ***tu es accro?** – are you addicted?*

2 **Complete the sentences in English, using the answers you ticked above.**

1 I buy things online _____ .

2 I read blogs _____ .

3 I play games online _____ .

4 I do research for my homework _____ .

5 I send emails _____ .

6 I do quizzes _____ .

3 **Look at your results below. Then write in English one thing that applies to you.**

Majorité de ◆	Tu es accro à Internet. Fais d'autres activités, par exemple du sport ou de la musique.
Majorité de ■	Tu n'es pas accro, mais fais attention: Internet est addictif!
Majorité de ▲	Tu n'aimes pas Internet. Mais c'est utile! Tu peux faire des recherches pour tes devoirs, par exemple.

5 Quand il fait beau, on va au parc (pages 16–17)

1 Circle the correct weather expression to match each weather symbol.

1 Quand il **pleut** / **fait chaud**, _____ .

2 Quand il fait **froid** / **chaud**, _____ .

3 Quand il fait **beau** / **froid**, _____ .

4 Quand il **fait froid** / **pleut**, _____ .

5 Quand il fait **chaud** / **froid**, _____ .

6 Quand il **fait beau** / **pleut**, _____ .

2 Now complete the sentences in exercise 1, choosing the correct phrase from the bubble to match each activity picture.

> on regarde des DVD
> on fait du VTT
> on va au café
> on joue au foot
> on va au cinéma
> on fait du bowling

on – *we*

3 Number the pictures in the order they appear in the text.

Quand <u>il pleut</u>, <u>je surfe sur Internet</u> avec mes copains. J'aime bien ça.

Quelquefois, on va <u>au cinéma</u> et on regarde un film. J'adore ça.

Quand <u>il fait chaud</u>, on va au parc et on fait <u>du skate</u> ou on joue <u>au basket.</u>
J'aime bien ça parce que je suis sportive mais je n'aime pas <u>le foot</u>. C'est nul!

1 Link the questions and answers.

Interview avec Amber – star de l'émission *Nouvelle Star*

1 Qu'est-ce que tu regardes à la télé?

2 Qu'est-ce que tu ne regardes pas?

3 Est-ce que tu aimes les émissions de sport?

4 Qu'est-ce que tu aimes comme films?

5 Qu'est-ce que tu lis en ce moment?

6 C'est bien?

7 Que fais-tu quand tu es connectée?

8 Qu'est-ce que tu fais quand tu es avec tes copains?

a J'adore les films fantastiques mais je n'aime pas les films d'horreur.

b Non, parce que je n'aime pas le sport. Je ne suis pas sportive.

c J'envoie des e-mails tous les jours et quelquefois, je fais des achats en ligne.

d Moi, je regarde les séries américaines et j'aime aussi les documentaires.

e Oui, à mon avis, c'est passionnant.

f Je ne regarde pas les infos. Je déteste ça, c'est barbant.

g On va au café ou au restaurant. J'adore les restaurants italiens!

h En ce moment, je lis un roman policier.

2 **Choose four of the questions and adapt the answers to answer them for yourself.**

_____

_____

_____

_____

3 Read all the forum entries. Put a
✔ next to each person's entry if
they liked the *Twilight* films and
a ✗ if they didn't.

> Don't worry about words you don't know.
> You should understand enough to say
> whether they liked the films or not.

Twilight – tu aimes ou pas?

annecb2
Moi, j'adore *Twilight* et j'aime tous les acteurs. J'ai regardé les deux
films *Fascination* et *Tentation* mais je n'ai pas regardé *Hésitation*.

mellec
Moi, j'ai regardé *Twilight 1* au ciné hier soir et j'ai trouvé
ça nul! Je n'aime pas les acteurs et je n'aime pas les films.
Je déteste les films fantastiques.

.g2
Moi, j'adore Robert Pattinson, c'est mon acteur préféré.
Je suis fan de *Twilight* parce que je suis fan de ses films!

rorymac
Moi, je n'ai pas aimé *Twilight*. C'est horrible! Je n'aime pas
les acteurs, je n'aime pas les effets spéciaux et je n'aime pas
Robert Pattinson. Non merci!!

4 Find and highlight the French phrases below in the text. Then match them
to the English, by using logic or by looking at the rest of the sentence.

effets spéciaux	all the actors
hier soir	I thought it was rubbish
tous les acteurs	special effects
je n'ai pas regardé	I didn't like
je n'ai pas aimé	I didn't watch
j'ai trouvé ça nul	last night

5 Read the forum entries again. Who …?

1 says that *Twilight* is horrible _____

2 has not seen the third film, *Hésitation* _____

3 says Robert Pattinson is his/her favourite actor _____

4 liked all the actors _____

5 didn't like the special effects _____

6 went to the cinema last night _____

7 hates fantasy films _____

8 doesn't like Robert Pattinson _____

À la télé • *On TV*

je regarde …	*I watch …*
les documentaires	*documentaries*
les émissions de sport	*sports programmes*
les émissions de télé-réalité	*reality TV shows*
les infos	*news*
les jeux télévisés	*game shows*
les séries	*series*
les séries policières	*police series*
les séries américaines	*American series*

Les adjectifs • *Adjectives*

grand	grande	*tall*
petit	petite	*small*
intelligent	intelligente	*intelligent*
beau	belle	*handsome/ beautiful*
amusant	amusante	*funny*
pauvre	pauvre	*poor*
gentil	gentille	*nice*
riche	riche	*rich*

Est-ce que tu aimes …? • *Do you like …?*

Oui, j'aime ça.	*Yes, I like that.*
Non, je n'aime pas ça.	*No, I don't like that.*
c'est …	*it's …*
amusant	*funny*
génial	*great*
intéressant	*interesting*
ennuyeux	*boring*
nul	*rubbish*
j'adore	*I love*
j'aime bien	*I like*
je n'aime pas	*I don't like*
je déteste	*I hate*
je ne regarde pas	*I don't watch*
J'ai une passion pour …	*I have a passion for …*
Je suis fan de …	*I am a fan of …*
Je ne suis pas fan de …	*I am not a fan of …*

Les films • *Films*

J'aime …	*I like …*
les comédies	*comedies*
les films d'action	*action films*
les films d'arts martiaux	*martial-arts films*
les films fantastiques	*fantasy films*
les films d'horreur	*horror films*
les films de science-fiction	*science fiction films*
les westerns	*westerns*
les dessins animés	*cartoons*
Qui est ton acteur préféré?	*Who is your favourite actor?*
Mon acteur préféré, c'est …	*My favourite actor is …*
Qui est ton actrice préférée?	*Who is your favourite actress?*
Mon actrice préférée, c'est …	*My favourite actress is …*
Quel est ton film préféré?	*What is your favourite film?*
Mon film préféré, c'est …	*My favourite film is …*

Vocabulaire

Cahier vert
Module 1

La lecture • *Reading*

Je lis …	I am reading …
une BD	a comic book
un livre sur les animaux	a book about animals
un livre d'épouvante	a horror story
un magazine sur les célébrités	a magazine about celebrities
un roman fantastique	a fantasy novel
un roman policier	a thriller
C'est bien?	Is it good?
À mon avis, c'est …	In my opinion it's …
assez bien	quite good
passionnant	exciting
Qui est ton auteur préféré?	Who is your favourite author?
Mon auteur préféré, c'est …	My favourite author is …

Le temps • *The weather*

Quand …	When …
il fait beau	it's nice
il fait froid	it's cold
il fait chaud	it's hot
il pleut	it's raining
on fait du VTT	we do mountain biking
on fait du skate	we do skateboarding
on fait du bowling	we go bowling
on regarde des DVD	we watch DVDs
on va …	we go …
au café	to the café
au cinéma	to the cinema
au parc	to the park
on joue …	we play …
au foot	football
au basket	basketball
on surfe sur Internet	we surf the internet
avec mes copains	with my friends

Sur Internet • *On the internet*

J'envoie des e-mails.	I send emails.
Je fais beaucoup de choses.	I do lots of things.
Je fais des recherches pour mes devoirs.	I do research for my homework.
Je fais des achats.	I buy things.
Je fais des quiz.	I do quizzes.
Je joue à des jeux en ligne.	I play games online.
Je lis des blogs.	I read blogs.
Je trouve ça …	I find it …
chouette	great
pratique	practical
stupide	stupid
barbant	boring

Les mots essentiels • *High-frequency words*

assez	quite
aussi	also
comme	as
et	and
mais	but
normalement	normally
parce que	because
par exemple	for example
quand	when
surtout	above all
très	very

Expressions of time and frequency

d'habitude	usually
en ce moment	at the moment
quelquefois	sometimes
souvent	often
tous les soirs	every evening
une fois par semaine	once a week

Studio 2 © Pearson Education Limited 2011

11

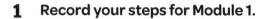

1 Record your steps for Module 1.

2 Look at the step descriptors on pages 62–63 and set your targets for Module 2.

3 Fill in what you need to do to achieve these targets.

Listening	I have reached _____ Step in **Listening**. In Module 2, I want to reach _____ Step. I need to _____ _____ _____ _____
Speaking	I have reached _____ Step in **Speaking**. In Module 2, I want to reach _____ Step. I need to _____ _____ _____ _____
Reading	I have reached _____ Step in **Reading**. In Module 2, I want to reach _____ Step. I need to _____ _____ _____ _____
Writing	I have reached _____ Step in **Writing**. In Module 2, I want to reach _____ Step. I need to _____ _____ _____ _____

Paris touristique (pages 28–29)

1 Read the two adverts and look at the pictures. Put a ✔ if the picture is mentioned in the text and a ✗ if it isn't.

1

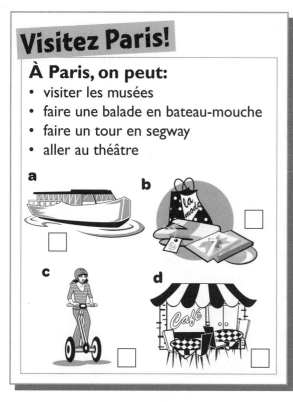

Visitez Paris!

À Paris, on peut:
- visiter les musées
- faire une balade en bateau-mouche
- faire un tour en segway
- aller au théâtre

2

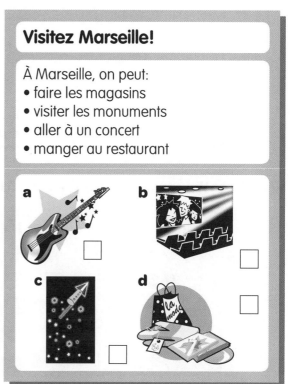

Visitez Marseille!

À Marseille, on peut:
- faire les magasins
- visiter les monuments
- aller à un concert
- manger au restaurant

2 Look at the pictures for Strasbourg and Nice. Complete an advert for each of them, using the phrases from exercise 1.

Visitez Strasbourg!

À Strasbourg, on peut:

_____

_____

_____

Visitez Nice!

À Nice, on peut:

_____

_____

_____

1 Complete the sentences with the correct words from the box.

Salut, je m'appelle Sophie!

1 Quelquefois, j'aime _____ des photos.

2 Mais je déteste faire du _____ , c'est nul.

3 Et je n'aime pas _____ au cinéma.

4 Moi, j'adore _____ mes copains en ville. C'est génial.

5 J'adore aussi aller aux concerts rock avec mes _____ .

6 J'aime aussi _____ les magasins avec ma mère.

> *faire   aller   copains   prendre   retrouver   roller*

2 Write the completed captions from exercise 1 under the correct pictures.

Sophie – la Goth!

a · Moi, j'adore retrouver …

3 Write two sentences about what you like and don't like doing by adapting the phrases above.

_____

_____

1 Use the code to complete the question words and phrases, then match them to the English.

★ = a	♣ = e	♥ = i	♦ = o	♠ = u

1 c♦mb♥♣n? _____

2 ♦♠? _____

3 q♠★nd? _____

4 ★ q♠♣ll♣ h♣♠r♣? _____

a at what time?

b when?

c how much?

d where?

2 Write the following questions in French by using one phrase from cloud A and one phrase from cloud B.

1 Where is the museum?   *C'est où, le musée?* _____

2 How much does it cost to get in? _____

3 When is it open? _____

4 What time is it open? _____

5 Is there a cafeteria? _____

6 Is there a souvenir shop? _____

A
Est-ce qu'il y a
C'est ouvert
C'est où,
Est-ce qu'il y a
C'est ouvert
C'est combien,

B
quand?
une cafétéria?
à quelle heure?
l'entrée?
une boutique de souvenirs?
le musée?

3 Read the leaflet about the Cité des sciences and answer the questions below.

1 Could you visit at 10 p.m. on a Tuesday? Why?

2 Could you visit at 10 a.m. on a Monday? Why?

3 Which two forms of transport are mentioned?

4 How much would it cost for two adults? _____

5 Who would pay €6? _____

6 What would you pay for a five-year-old? _____

Visitez la Cité des sciences et de l'industrie!

30 avenue Corentin-Cariou
75019 Paris

Horaires:
Ouverte du mardi au samedi de 9h30 à 18h
Ouverte le dimanche de 9h45 à 19h
Fermée le lundi

Accès:
Métro: Ligne 7 station Porte de la Villette
Autobus: lignes 139, 150, 152

Tarifs d'entrée:
Adultes: 8€
–25 ans: 6€
–6 ans: gratuit

Studio 2 © Pearson Education Limited 2011

1 Find eight opinions in the smiley and write them under the symbols below.

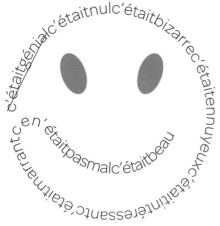

> To give an opinion in the past, use
> **C'était ...**, e.g.
> **C'était marrant.** – It was fun.
> To say 'I visited ...', use **J'ai visité ...**, e.g.
> **J'ai visité la tour Eiffel.**

☺	☹	😐
C'était génial.		

2 Say that you visited each of the places below and describe what it was like.

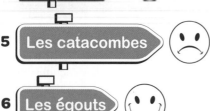

1 L'Arc de Triomphe ☺ J'ai visité l'Arc de Triomphe. C'était génial.

2 Le Centre Pompidou ☹ _____

3 La tour Eiffel ☺ _____

4 Notre-Dame 😐 _____

5 Les catacombes ☹ _____

6 Les égouts ☺ _____

 1 Unjumble the following sentences and write them by the correct picture.

a restaurant mangé J'ai au
b des J'ai souvenirs acheté
c beaucoup dansé J'ai
d envoyé J'ai des postales cartes
e passé le Paris 14 J'ai juillet à
f le J'ai défilé regardé
g rencontré J'ai une fille jolie

 To say what you did in the past, use **J'ai** + past participle, e.g.
J'ai mangé ... – I ate ...
J'ai acheté ... – I bought ...

1 J'ai passé le 14 juillet à Paris. _____

2 _____ _____

3 _____ _____

4 _____ _____

5 _____ _____

6 _____ _____

7 _____ _____

2 Nathan Négatif doesn't do anything on 14th July. Change the sentences above for Nathan to say what he <u>didn't</u> do.

 To say 'I did not do something' in the past, use **Je n'ai pas** + past participle, e.g.
Je n'ai pas mangé ...
Je n'ai pas rencontré ...

1 Je n'ai pas passé le 14 juillet à Paris. _____
2 _____
3 _____
4 _____
5 _____
6 _____
7 _____

1 Complete the crossword with the missing words from the email. Use the words in the box.

Salut Sophie!

J'ai passé le 14 (**6**) _____ à Paris. C'était génial!

D'abord, j'ai (**4**) _____ la tour Eiffel, c'était (**1**) _____ .

Puis j'ai (**5**) _____ au restaurant à la tour Eiffel.

J'ai (**8**) _____ des souvenirs et j'ai envoyé des

(**7**) _____ postales.

Ensuite, j'ai (**2**) _____ le défilé et après, j'ai beaucoup

(**9**) _____ .

J'ai aussi (**10**) _____ un garçon qui (**3**) _____

Hugo. Il est très beau.

Danielle

| mangé | regardé | juillet | s'appelle | dansé |
| acheté | visité | marrant | cartes | rencontré |

1. _ r _ _ _ _ _ _
2. _ e _ _ _ _ _ _ _ _
3. _ s _ _ _ _ _ _
4. _ _ _ _ t _ _ _
5. _ a _ _ _
6. _ u _ _ _ _
7. _ r _ _ _
8. _ a _ _ _ _
9. _ n _ _ _
10. _ _ _ _ t _ _

2 Read Danielle's email again and answer the questions.

1 When did Danielle go to Paris? _____

2 What did she visit first? _____

3 Where did she eat? _____

4 What did she do after eating? _____

5 What did she do after watching the parade? _____

6 Who does she mention at the end? _____

3 **Highlight in the two texts the French for the English expressions below.**

Paris, c'est super! D'abord, samedi matin à huit heures, j'ai visité Notre–Dame, et puis à midi, j'ai mangé au restaurant. Le soir, à sept heures, j'ai regardé la télé. Dimanche à neuf heures, j'ai visité la tour Eiffel, et après, j'ai fait les magasins et j'ai acheté des souvenirs.
Odile

Quel weekend j'ai passé à Paris! Samedi soir, j'ai regardé le feu d'artifice et j'ai dansé jusqu'à minuit.
Puis dimanche matin à dix heures, j'ai visité le Louvre, et ensuite, j'ai envoyé des cartes postales. Au Louvre, j'ai rencontré une jolie fille, c'était super!
Sam

1	I visited	**2**	I ate	**3**	I watched	**4**	I bought
5	I spent	**6**	I danced	**7**	I sent	**8**	I met

4 **Does this note belong to Odile or Sam?**

_____

Saturday
Evening: fireworks

Sunday
10:00 Louvre
After: sent postcards

5 **Complete this note in English for the other person.**

Saturday
8:00 _____
12:00 _____
7:00 _____
Sunday
9:00 _____
After: _____

6 **Complete the following sentences to write a short paragraph about your visit to Paris.**

Paris, c'est génial. D'abord, samedi matin, j'ai visité _____

À midi, j'ai _____

Le soir, j'ai _____

Dimanche à dix heures, j'ai _____

Après, j'ai _____

Finalement, j'ai _____

Use sentences from the texts and just change one detail, e.g.
samedi matin à <u>huit</u> heures → samedi matin à <u>neuf</u> heures
j'ai visité <u>Notre–Dame</u> → j'ai visité <u>les égouts</u>

Qu'est-ce qu'on peut faire?
• *What can you do?*

On peut …	*You can …*
aller à un concert	*go to a concert*
aller au théâtre	*go to the theatre*
faire les magasins	*go shopping*
faire un tour en segway	*go on a tour by segway*
faire une balade en bateau-mouche	*go on a boat trip*
manger au restaurant	*eat in a restaurant*
visiter les monuments	*visit the monuments*
visiter les musées	*visit the museums*

D'accord? • *Do you agree?*

À mon avis …	*In my opinion …*
c'est vrai	*it's true*
c'est faux	*it's false*
Je suis d'accord.	*I agree.*
Je ne suis pas d'accord.	*I disagree.*

J'aime … • *I like …*

J'adore …	*I love …*
Je n'aime pas …	*I don't like …*
Je déteste …	*I hate …*
aller au cinéma (avec mes amis)	*going to the cinema (with my friends)*
aller aux concerts (rock)	*going to (rock) concerts*
aller voir des matchs (au Parc des Princes)	*going to watch matches (at the Parc des Princes)*
faire du roller (au Trocadéro)	*roller-blading (at the Trocadéro)*
faire les magasins	*going shopping*
prendre des photos	*taking photos*
retrouver mes copains	*meeting up with my mates*

Des questions touristiques
• *Tourist questions*

C'est où, le musée?	*Where is the museum?*
C'est ouvert quand?	*When is it open? (day or date)*
C'est ouvert à quelle heure?	*At what time is it open?*
C'est combien, l'entrée?	*How much does it cost to get in?*
Est-ce qu'il y a …	*Is there …*
une cafétéria/une boutique de souvenirs?	*a cafeteria/a souvenir shop?*

Studio 2 © Pearson Education Limited 2011

Vocabulaire

ahier vert
Module 2

Des informations touristiques • *Tourist information*

horaires d'ouverture	*opening times*
ouvert tous les jours	*open every day*
sauf le lundi	*except Mondays*
ouvert du (mardi) au (dimanche)	*open from (Tuesday) to (Sunday)*
fermé	*closed*
de 10h00 à 17h00	*from 10 a.m. to 5 p.m.*
tarifs d'entrée	*admission prices*
adultes	*adults*
jeunes	*young people*
enfants	*children*
gratuit	*free*
Il y a (une cafétéria).	*There is (a cafeteria).*
Il n'y a pas de (boutique de souvenirs).	*There isn't a (souvenir shop).*

À Paris • *In Paris*

J'ai passé le 14 juillet à Paris.	*I spent the 14th July in Paris.*
J'ai acheté des souvenirs.	*I bought some souvenirs.*
J'ai (beaucoup) dansé.	*I danced (a lot).*
J'ai envoyé des cartes postales.	*I sent postcards.*
J'ai mangé au restaurant.	*I ate in a restaurant.*
J'ai regardé le défilé/le feu d'artifice.	*I watched the parade/the fireworks.*
J'ai rencontré un beau garçon/une jolie fille.	*I met a good-looking boy/a pretty girl.*
J'ai visité ...	*I visited ...*
le musée du Louvre/la tour Eiffel/les catacombes	*the Louvre museum/the Eiffel Tower/the Catacombs*

C'était comment? • *What was it like?*

C'était ...	*It was ...*
beau	*beautiful*
bizarre	*weird*
ennuyeux	*boring*
génial	*great*
intéressant	*interesting*
marrant	*funny/a laugh*
nul	*rubbish*
Ce n'était pas mal.	*It wasn't bad.*

Les mots essentiels • *High-frequency words*

à quelle heure?	*when?/at what time?*
quand?	*when? (for day, month, year, etc.)*
combien?	*how much?/how many?*
où?	*where?*
un peu	*a bit*
beaucoup (de)	*a lot (of)*
d'abord	*first of all*
ensuite	*next*
puis	*then*
après	*afterwards*
finalement	*finally/lastly*

tudio 2 © Pearson Education Limited 2011

21

1 **Record your steps for Module 2.**

2 **Look at the step descriptors on pages 62–63 and set your targets for Module 3.**

3 **Fill in what you need to do to achieve these targets.**

Listening 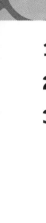	I have reached _____ Step in **Listening**. In Module 3, I want to reach _____ Step. I need to _____ _____ _____ _____
Speaking *Salut!*	I have reached _____ Step in **Speaking**. In Module 3, I want to reach _____ Step. I need to _____ _____ _____ _____
Reading	I have reached _____ Step in **Reading**. In Module 3, I want to reach _____ Step. I need to _____ _____ _____ _____
Writing	I have reached _____ Step in **Writing**. In Module 3, I want to reach _____ Step. I need to _____ _____ _____ _____

1 Find and write out the French adjectives to match the English.

1 lazy _____
2 nice _____
3 patient _____
4 shy _____
5 annoying _____
6 selfish _____
7 funny _____
8 sporty _____
9 intelligent _____

2 Read about Amina's friendship group and write the correct name under each picture.

Dans ma bande, nous sommes quatre: deux garçons et deux filles!

D'abord, il y a **Hugo**. Il est très drôle et assez intelligent. Il est un peu égoïste. Il aime la musique.

Puis il y a **Sarah**. Elle est très sympa et très patiente. Elle aime retrouver ses copains. Elle est un peu paresseuse.

Finalement, **Noah**! Il est sportif mais il est un peu pénible. Quelquefois, il est un peu timide. Il adore le sport.

a  _____

b  _____

c  _____

3 Complete the grid of adjectives below. All the missing words are in the texts.

English	Masculine	Feminine
intelligent		intelligente
funny		drôle
kind	sympa	
patient	patient	
lazy	paresseux	
sporty		sportive
shy		timide

 Most adjectives are different in the feminine form but some stay the same.

1 Copy the sentences below the correct picture.

> On va en ville.
> On parle de mode.
> On fait du shopping.
> On parle de sport.
> On écoute de la musique.
> On joue à des jeux vidéo.

1

_____

2

_____

5

_____

3

_____

6

_____

4

_____

2 Read the text and then circle the correct options in the English sentences.

Ma bande de copains

Je fais beaucoup de choses avec mes copains. Le samedi, on va en ville et on va au café. Quand il pleut, on joue à des jeux vidéo ou on joue à des jeux en ligne. C'est génial. J'adore ça.

Quand il fait beau, on va au parc et on joue au football. J'aime bien ça parce que je suis très sportif. En général, avec mes copains, on parle de sport ou de films. *Tom*

1 On Saturdays Tom goes **into town** / **shopping** / **to the pool**.

2 He also goes to **a match** / **the café** / **the park**.

3 When it's **cold** / **raining** / **hot** he plays video games.

4 He also **does quizzes** / **reads blogs** / **plays online games**.

5 When it's nice he **goes to the park** / **plays tennis** / **goes cycling**.

6 He **doesn't like** / **hates** / **likes** sport.

7 He and his friends talk about **sport and fashion** / **fashion and films** / **sport and films**.

1 Unjumble the words in the following sentences about music.

1 du J'écoute jazz   *J'écoute du jazz.*

2 rap du J'écoute   _____

3 de musique J'écoute classique la   _____

4 les J'adore mélodies   _____

5 la d'Ellie Goulding musique J'aime   _____

6 n'aime Je pas la des musique Black Eyed Peas   _____

7 groupe Gorillaz préféré, Mon c'est   _____

8 chanteur Mon Raphaël préféré, c'est   _____

2 Read the following forum entries and then note whether the sentences below are true (✔) or false (✘).

> **Fifi22**
> Ma chanteuse préférée, c'est Ellie Goulding. J'aime beaucoup la chanson *Lights*, c'est génial! Je n'aime pas le jazz.

> **XSKid**
> Mon groupe préféré, c'est Muse parce que j'aime les paroles. J'adore la musique rock et j'écoute de la musique tous les soirs.

> **Miss soso**
> Moi, j'adore la musique de Diam's. Elle est chanteuse de rap. J'aime les paroles, c'est intéressant.

> **Émilie88**
> Mon groupe préféré, c'est MGMT, parce que j'aime les mélodies, mais j'écoute beaucoup d'artistes différents.

1 Fifi22's favourite group is Muse. ☐

2 She likes jazz. ☐

3 XSKid likes the words of Muse's songs. ☐

4 He doesn't listen to music much. ☐

5 Miss soso says Diam's is a jazz singer. ☐

6 She says Diam's words are interesting. ☐

7 Émilie88 likes MGMT's tunes. ☐

8 She only likes listening to MGMT. ☐

3 Write a forum entry using the following prompts. Adapt sentences from exercise 2.

- groupe préféré: JLS
- paroles
- écoute artistes différents

Mon groupe préféré, c'est _____

_____

_____

1 Complete the clothes labels with the words from the box.

une veste	un tee-shirt
des baskets	des bottes
un pantalon	une jupe
un sweat à capuche	un jean
des chaussures de skate	

2 Read the grammar box first! Then choose a colour from the boxes below to add to each clothes label in exercise 1. Finally, colour each item of clothing correctly.

1   bleu   orange   blanches

2   vert   marron   vert kaki

3   bleue   marron   noires

Studio Grammaire

Singular		Plural	
Masc	**Fem**	**Masc**	**Fem**
vert	verte	verts	vertes
blanc	blanche	blancs	blanches

marron and *orange* don't change.

3 You are going to a fancy dress party. Choose one of the following characters and describe and draw what you are going to wear.

DRACULA   Joueur/euse de basket   Top-modèle

Ce weekend, je vais porter un jean noir avec un pull noir et une veste noire. Je suis Dracula!

5 Le weekend dernier (pages 56–57)

1 Find the French in the text for the items listed below.

> Salut! Je m'appelle Matteo et j'habite à Strasbourg. Je suis sportif et patient mais je suis un peu paresseux. Je suis fan de tennis, c'est mon sport préféré. J'ai deux sœurs et un demi-frère.
>
> Le weekend dernier, je suis allé au stade Roland-Garros avec Tom et j'ai regardé le match de tennis Tsonga contre Murray. J'ai aimé le match, parce que Tsonga a gagné! Après le match, je suis allé au restaurant où j'ai mangé une pizza. C'était super-cool!

1 sport _____

2 words to describe his character _____

2 family members _____

2 places he went to _____

1 food item _____

2 Find the following verbs in the text. (Clue: they all follow *je*.)

Present	Past
I'm called	I went
_____	_____
I live	I watched
_____	_____
I am	I liked
_____	_____
I have	I ate
_____	_____

Studio Grammaire

Present	Past
je regarde	j'**ai** regard**é**
je vais	je **suis** all**é(e)**

3 Write a short passage. Use Matteo's text from exercise 1 and change at least eight words.

Salut! Je m'appelle Julien et j'habite à ...

_____

_____

_____

_____

_____

> Julien/Juliette
> intelligent(e), timide
> basket
> une sœur, deux frères
> weekend dernier: match à Paris
> après: café

Interview avec Candice Cool

1 Complete the puzzle with the missing words from Candice's answers. Use the words in the box.

Réponses

1 J'  du pop rock.

2 On fait du  .

3 Je vais au restaurant.

4 Je suis assez  et très sympa.

5 Je vais porter une jupe, un tee-shirt et des noires.

6 Je suis allée à un  avec mes copains.

concert   shopping   écoute
bottes   sportive   manger

1		c					
2		h				
		a				
3		n				
4		s				
5		o			
6		n			

2 Note the number of the answer from exercise 1 which goes with each question.

Questions

a Décris ton caractère. ☐

b Quelle musique écoutes-tu? ☐

c Qu'est-ce que tu vas faire ce weekend? ☐

d Qu'est-ce que tu vas porter? ☐

e Qu'est-ce que tu as fait le weekend dernier? ☐

f Tu fais quoi avec tes copains? ☐

3 Adapt Candice's answers to write your own answer to each question.

a Je suis assez _____ et très _____ .

4 Match up the French and English time expressions below. Then write the French expressions in the correct column of the grid.

hier
aujourd'hui
le weekend dernier
en ce moment
comme d'hab
hier soir

at the moment
last weekend
yesterday
last night
as usual
today

Present	Past
aujourd'hui	

5 Read the texts and write the names in the grid below according to who is doing or has done each activity.

Salim

Aujourd'hui, je vais au match de foot. J'adore le foot! Hier, j'ai regardé un match de basket, c'était super!

Hier, j'ai écouté de la musique au concert. J'adore le jazz. Aujourd'hui, je vais au café avec mes amis.

Malika

Julie

D'habitude, le samedi, je vais à la discothèque, mais hier, j'ai regardé un match de foot. C'était génial.

Hier, je suis allé au café où j'ai mangé un sandwich. Aujourd'hui, je joue au basket.

Laurent

Charlotte

En ce moment, j'écoute de la musique rock. J'adore ça! Hier, je suis allée à la discothèque au collège avec ma copine. C'était marrant!

	Present	Past
🏀		
⚽	Salim	
♪		
🏪		

> **Two ways to recognise present or past.**
> • Look for time expressions (see exercise 4).
> • Look at the verbs:
>
> | Present | Past |
> |---|---|
> | je regarde | j'ai regardé |
> | je vais | je suis allé(e) |
> | j'écoute | j'ai écouté |
> | je mange | j'ai mangé |

Vocabulaire

Mon caractère • *My character*

Je suis …	*I am …*
Tu es …	*You are …*
Il est …	*He is …*
Elle est …	*She is …*
Je ne suis pas …	*I'm not …*
drôle	*funny*
égoïste	*selfish*
intelligent(e)	*intelligent*
paresseux/paresseuse	*lazy*
patient(e)	*patient*
pénible	*annoying*
sportif/sportive	*sporty*
sympa	*nice*
timide	*shy*
mon frère	*my brother*
ma sœur	*my sister*
mes parents	*my parents*
mon meilleur ami	*my best friend (male)*
ma meilleure amie	*my best friend (female)*

Ma bande de copains • *My group of friends*

Tu fais quoi avec tes copains/copines?	*What do you do with your friends?*
On écoute de la musique.	*We listen to music.*
On joue à des jeux vidéo.	*We play video games.*
On va en ville.	*We go into town.*
On fait du shopping.	*We go shopping.*
On rigole.	*We have fun.*
Tu parles de quoi avec tes copains?	*What do you talk about with your friends?*
On parle de sport.	*We talk about sport.*
On parle de mode.	*We talk about fashion.*
On parle de films.	*We talk about films.*
Je fais beaucoup de choses.	*I do lots of things.*
On s'entend très bien.	*We get on very well.*

La musique • *Music*

Quelle musique écoutes-tu?	*What music do you listen to?*
J'écoute du R'n'B.	*I listen to R'n'B.*
J'écoute du rap.	*I listen to rap.*
J'écoute du jazz.	*I listen to jazz.*
J'écoute du pop-rock.	*I listen to pop.*
J'écoute de la musique classique.	*I listen to classical music.*
J'écoute beaucoup d'artistes différents.	*I listen to lots of different artists.*
J'aime la musique de X.	*I like X's music.*
Je n'aime pas la musique de X.	*I don't like X's music.*
Mon groupe préféré, c'est …	*My favourite group is …*
Mon chanteur préféré, c'est …	*My favourite (male) singer is …*
Ma chanteuse préférée, c'est …	*My favourite (female) singer is …*
J'adore la chanson …	*I love the song …*
les mélodies	*the tunes*
les paroles	*the words*

Les vêtements • *Clothes*

Qu'est-ce que tu vas porter à la fête?	*What are you going to wear to the party?*
Je vais porter ...	*I'm going to wear ...*
des baskets	*trainers*
des bottes	*boots*
des chaussures (de skate)	*(skater) shoes*
une chemise	*a shirt*
un jean	*jeans*
une jupe	*a skirt*
un pantalon	*trousers*
un pull	*a jumper*
un sweat à capuche	*a hoodie*
un tee-shirt	*a T-shirt*
une veste	*a jacket*
les vêtements	*clothes*

Les couleurs • *Colours*

beige	*beige*
blanc(he)	*white*
bleu(e)	*blue*
marron	*brown*
noir(e)	*black*
orange	*orange*
vert kaki	*khaki*

Ce weekend • *This weekend*

Ce weekend, je vais ...	*This weekend I'm going ...*
manger au restaurant	*to eat in a restaurant*
aller en ville	*to go into town*
jouer au foot	*to play football*
faire du camping	*to go camping*
aller au cinéma	*to go to the cinema*
faire de la rando	*to go hiking*

Le weekend dernier • *Last weekend*

je suis allé(e) au stade	*I went to the stadium*
je suis allé(e) au parc	*I went to the park*
je suis allé(e) au café	*I went to the café*
je suis allé(e) en ville	*I went into town*
je suis allé(e) à un concert	*I went to a concert*
je suis allé(e) à la piscine	*I went to the swimming pool*
je suis allé(e) à Paris	*I went to Paris*
je suis allé(e) à la discothèque	*I went to the disco*
j'ai mangé des frites	*I ate chips*
j'ai écouté de la musique	*I listened to music*
j'ai regardé un match de foot	*I watched a football match*
j'ai dansé	*I danced*
j'ai joué au tennis	*I played tennis*
j'ai visité le musée du Louvre	*I visited the Louvre museum*
j'ai acheté un jean	*I bought a pair of jeans*
j'ai nagé	*I swam*

Les mots essentiels • *High-frequency words*

alors	*so*
avec	*with*
bien	*well*
comme d'hab	*as usual*
en général	*in general*
ensemble	*together*
ouah!	*wow!*
où	*where*
ou	*or*
si	*if*
tout(e)	*all, every*
tout le temps	*all the time*
vraiment	*really*

1 Record your steps for Module 3.

2 Look at the step descriptors on pages 62–63 and set your targets for Module 4.

3 Fill in what you need to do to achieve these targets.

Listening	I have reached _____ Step in **Listening**. In Module 4, I want to reach _____ Step. I need to _____ _____ _____ _____
Speaking	I have reached _____ Step in **Speaking**. In Module 4, I want to reach _____ Step. I need to _____ _____ _____ _____
Reading	I have reached _____ Step in **Reading**. In Module 4, I want to reach _____ Step. I need to _____ _____ _____ _____
Writing	I have reached _____ Step in **Writing**. In Module 4, I want to reach _____ Step. I need to _____ _____ _____ _____

1 **Look at the pictures and read the sentences. Who's speaking?**

Stéphanie

Julien

Nabila

Thomas

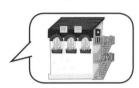

Lucie

Raphaël

1 J'habite dans un grand appartement.
Lucie

2 J'habite dans un petit village.
_____

3 J'habite dans une petite maison.
_____

4 J'habite dans une grande ville.
_____

5 J'habite dans un petit appartement.
_____

6 J'habite dans une grande maison.
_____

2 **Write a sentence for each person, saying where they <u>would like</u> to live. Use phrases from the tip box.**

1 Stéphanie

Je voudrais habiter dans une vieille chaumière.

6 Raphaël

_____
_____
_____

2 Julien

_____
_____
_____

3 Nabila

_____
_____
_____

4 Thomas

_____
_____
_____

5 Lucie

_____
_____
_____

> **!** *To say 'I would like to live' somewhere, use:*
>
> | | |
> |---|---|
> | *Je voudrais habiter* | *au bord de la mer* |
> | | *dans une ~~vieille chaumière~~* |
> | | *à la montagne* |
> | | *dans une ferme* |
> | | *à la campagne* |
> | | *dans un vieux château* |

1 Label the rooms of the flat with the words on the right.

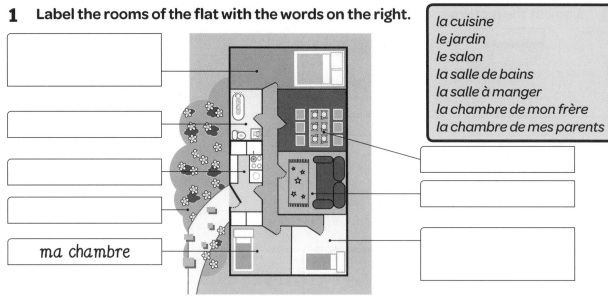

la cuisine
le jardin
le salon
la salle de bains
la salle à manger
la chambre de mon frère
la chambre de mes parents

ma chambre

2 Answer the questions, saying where the animals are. Use the prepositions in the box and the grid below to help you.

1 Où est la souris?

sur l'armoire

2 Où est le rat?

_____
_____

3 Où est le chat?

_____
_____

4 Où est la tortue?

_____
_____

5 Où est le chien?

_____
_____

6 Où est le lapin?

_____
_____

7 Où est le hamster?

_____
_____

dans – in
derrière – behind
devant – in front of
sous – under
sur – on

dans	
derrière	le lit
devant	l'armoire
sous	le bureau
sur	

1 **Read the texts and tick the correct items in the grid for each person.**

Sarah			✔					
Laïla								

> D'habitude, pour le petit déjeuner, je bois du lait et je prends du pain avec du beurre et de la confiture. Quelquefois, je prends du jus d'orange. *Sarah*

> Je prends des céréales pour le petit déjeuner en semaine et je bois du chocolat chaud. Quelquefois, le weekend, je bois du lait et je mange un croissant. *Laïla*

2 **Complete the passages with the correct word for 'some' (*du/de la/des*).**

> Le soir, on mange à huit heures. Mon plat préféré, c'est _____ poisson avec _____ pâtes et comme dessert, _____ glace! *Sarah*

Studio Grammaire
To say 'some':
masc: **du** *poisson, poulet*
fem: **de la** *viande, glace, pizza*
plural: **des** *pâtes, plats, fruits*

> D'habitude, le soir, on mange _____ viande. Hier soir, je suis allée au restaurant et j'ai mangé _____ poulet. Comme dessert, j'ai mangé _____ fruits et une mousse au chocolat! *Laïla*

3 **Write what you usually have for breakfast and what you eat on a Saturday evening, using the pictures.**

D'habitude, pour le petit déjeuner,

je bois _____

_____

et je prends _____

Le samedi, on prend _____

_____

Comme dessert, on mange _____

_____

Studio 2 © Pearson Education Limited 2011

4 C'est la Chandeleur! (pages 74–75)

1 Find and write out the French expressions to match pictures 1–6.

a unkilodebananes   b 500gdefromage   c quatretranchesdejambon   d unpaquetdefarine

e unetablettedechocolat   f unlitredelait

1  b 500g de fromage

2 _____

3 _____

4  _____

5 _____

6 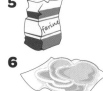 _____

2 Read the invitation and complete the notes in English.

Demain, c'est mon anniversaire! Tu es invité(e) à manger chez moi à huit heures.

On va manger des crêpes: des crêpes au fromage, au chocolat, aux bananes, tu peux choisir! Après, on peut regarder des DVD ou écouter de la musique. Alors, il faut apporter un DVD et des CD.

Samuel

- Occasion:
- Time:
- Going to eat:
- Activities after food:
- Need to bring:

3 Write an invitation to your party.

Demain, c'est mon anniversaire! Tu es invité(e) à manger

 Adapt the invitation in exercise 2. Change the details of food, time, activities, etc. Use the following phrases if you wish:
- **sept heures et demie**
- **de la pizza au fromage / au jambon**
- **aller au cinéma / jouer sur ma Playstation**
- **apporter de l'argent / des jeux de console**

1 Using the spider diagram, write a sentence about each picture.

boire un coca   regarder le feu d'artifice

prendre des photos   **Je vais**   manger au restaurant

danser   chanter

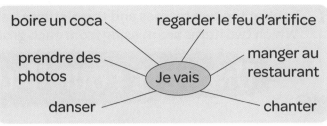

1

Je vais danser.

2

_____

5

_____

3

_____

6

_____

4

_____

> *Use **Je vais** + infinitive to say what you're going to do, e.g.*
> ***Je vais aller au carnaval.** – I'm going to go to the carnival.*

2 Read the texts about the carnival. Who mentions each picture? Write the correct name.

J'habite à Dunkerque, dans le nord de la France. La semaine prochaine, je vais aller au carnaval avec ma famille. On va regarder le défilé et je vais danser. Après, on va aller au restaurant. Je vais manger une crêpe et je vais boire de la limonade. *Léo*

Moi, j'habite à Nice. Cette année, je vais participer au défilé et je vais jouer de la flûte dans un groupe. Je vais porter un costume de pirate! Après, je vais regarder le feu d'artifice. On va s'amuser! *Delphine*

1 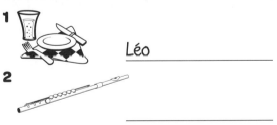   Léo

2

_____

3

_____

4

5

_____

6

_____

7

_____

1 Look at the two recipes and the pictures below them.
Which two items are missing from each group of pictures?

UNE FÊTE POUR HALLOWEEN!

Un cocktail de vampire
Il faut:
un litre de limonade
un litre de jus d'orange
2 citrons
½ litre de jus de pomme

Un gâteau de sorcière
Il faut:
200g de beurre
600g de farine
3 œufs
200g de sucre
de la crème Chantilly

Missing:

_____

_____

Missing:

_____

_____

2 Read the Halloween invitation and answer the questions in English.

Tu es invité(e) à une fête pour Halloween chez moi samedi soir.
• Tu peux porter un costume de fantôme, de sorcière ou de vampire!
• On va boire un cocktail de vampire et on va manger un gâteau de sorcière.
• Après, on va regarder un film d'horreur.
• Il faut arriver chez moi à sept heures.
Camille

1 What is the event? _____
2 When is the party taking place? _____
3 What do you have to wear? _____
4 What are you going to drink? _____
5 What are you going to eat? _____
6 What are you going to do afterwards? _____
7 What time do you have to arrive? _____

3 Challenge yourself! Spend two minutes reading the text. Can you find out six facts?

Ma fête préférée, c'est Halloween. Halloween, c'est le 31 octobre. En France, pour Halloween, on porte des costumes de fantôme, de vampire et de squelette. C'est très effrayant mais c'est marrant!

Ce weekend, j'ai invité douze copains chez moi. On va manger des pizzas. Je vais préparer un cocktail de vampire et un gâteau de sorcière!

Après, on va regarder un DVD – un film d'horreur – et on va écouter de la musique. Moi, je vais porter un costume de sorcière: une cape noire avec un chapeau de sorcière.

Camille

4 Link the French to the English.

1	my favourite festival	**a**	c'est très effrayant
2	ghost	**b**	vampire
3	vampire	**c**	j'ai invité
4	skeleton	**d**	ma fête préférée
5	it's very frightening	**e**	fantôme
6	I have invited	**f**	squelette
7	a witch's costume	**g**	une cape noire
8	a black cape	**h**	un chapeau de sorcière
9	a witch's hat	**i**	un costume de sorcière

> *Don't worry if there are words you don't understand. Work out new words by:*
> - *making sensible guesses*
> - *finding words which look like English words*
> - *using the pictures as clues*
> - *using what you know about Halloween.*

5 Number the pictures 1–8 in the order in which they are mentioned in the text.

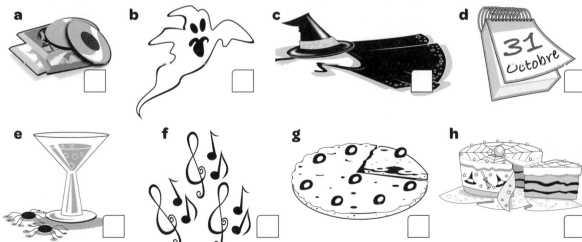

a b c d

e f g h

Les domiciles • *Homes*

J'habite dans …	*I live in …*
une grande maison	*a big house*
une petite maison	*a small house*
un grand appartement	*a big flat*
un petit appartement	*a small flat*
une grande ville	*a big town*
une petite ville	*a small town*
un grand village	*a big village*
un petit village	*a small village*
Je voudrais habiter …	*I'd like to live …*
à la campagne	*in the country*
à la montagne	*in the mountains*
au bord de la mer	*at the seaside*
dans un vieux château	*in an old castle*
dans une vieille chaumière	*in an old cottage*
dans une ferme	*on a farm*

Les pièces • *Rooms*

Chez moi, il y a …	*In my home, there is/ there are …*
(six) pièces	*(six) rooms*
le salon	*the living room*
le jardin	*the garden*
la cuisine	*the kitchen*
la salle à manger	*the dining room*
la salle de bains	*the bathroom*
ma chambre	*my bedroom*
la chambre de (mes parents/ma sœur/ mon frère)	*(my parents'/ my sister's/ my brother's) bedroom*
Il n'y a pas de (jardin).	*There isn't a (garden).*

Les prépositions • *Prepositions*

dans	*in*
devant	*in front of*
derrière	*behind*
sous	*under(neath)*
sur	*on*

Les meubles • *Furniture*

le bureau	*desk*
le canapé	*settee/sofa*
le lit	*bed*
le frigo	*fridge*
l'armoire (f)	*wardrobe*
la chaise	*chair*
la machine à laver	*washing machine*
le lavabo	*wash basin*
la douche	*shower*
la fenêtre	*window*
la table	*table*
la télé-satellite	*satellite TV*

Le petit déjeuner • *Breakfast*

Pour le petit déjeuner, je prends …	*For breakfast, I have …*
du beurre	*butter*
du café	*coffee*
du chocolat chaud	*hot chocolate*
du jus d'orange	*orange juice*
du lait	*milk*
du pain	*bread*
du thé	*tea*
de la confiture	*jam*
des céréales	*cereal*
une tartine	*a slice of bread and butter*
Je ne mange rien.	*I don't eat anything.*

Le dîner • *Evening meal*

D'habitude, on mange …	*Usually, we eat …*
du poisson	*fish*
du poulet	*chicken*
de la pizza	*pizza*
de la viande	*meat*
des fruits	*fruit*
des pâtes	*pasta*
des plats à emporter	*takeaway food*
Comme dessert, je prends …	*For dessert, I have …*
du yaourt	*yoghurt*
une mousse au chocolat	*a chocolate mousse*
de la glace (à la fraise)	*(strawberry) ice-cream*
Je suis végétarien(ne).	*I'm a vegetarian.*
Le soir, on mange à (six heures).	*In the evening, we eat at (six o'clock).*

Au carnaval • *At the carnival*

je vais …/on va …	*I'm going to …/ we're going to …*
aller au carnaval	*go to the carnival*
boire un coca	*drink a cola*
chanter et danser (sur le char)	*sing and dance (on the float)*
manger au restaurant	*eat in a restaurant*
participer au défilé	*take part in the parade*
porter un costume de (pirate)	*wear a (pirate) costume*
prendre des photos (avec mon portable)	*take photos (on my mobile phone)*
regarder le défilé/le feu d'artifice	*watch the parade/the fireworks*
Je vais m'amuser.	*I'm going to have fun.*
On va s'amuser.	*We're going to have fun.*

Les provisions • *Food shopping*

il faut acheter …	*I/we/you need to buy …*
un litre de lait	*a litre of milk*
un paquet de farine	*a packet of flour*
(quatre) tranches de jambon	*(four) slices of ham*
un kilo de bananes	*a kilo of bananas*
500 grammes de pommes	*500 grams of apples*
250 grammes de fraises	*250 grams of strawberries*
une tablette de chocolat	*a bar of chocolate*
une bombe de crème Chantilly	*a spray can of whipped cream*
six œufs	*six eggs*

Les mots essentiels • *High-frequency words*

chez (moi)	*at (my) place*
comme dessert	*for dessert*
il y a …	*there is/there are …*
il n'y a pas de …	*there isn't a/ any …*
ne … rien	*nothing*
pour	*for*

Studio 2 © Pearson Education Limited 2011

1 **Record your steps for Module 4.**

2 **Look at the step descriptors on pages 62–63 and set your targets for Module 5.**

3 **Fill in what you need to do to achieve these targets.**

Listening	I have reached _____ Step in **Listening**. In Module 5, I want to reach _____ Step. I need to _____
Speaking	I have reached _____ Step in **Speaking**. In Module 5, I want to reach _____ Step. I need to _____
Reading	I have reached _____ Step in **Reading**. In Module 5, I want to reach _____ Step. I need to _____
Writing	I have reached _____ Step in **Writing**. In Module 5, I want to reach _____ Step. I need to _____

1 Write a sentence for each picture, using a phrase from the grid.

1  Mon talent, c'est jouer du piano.

5 _____

6  _____

2 _____

3 _____

4 _____

	jouer du piano
	danser
Mon talent, c'est	faire de la magie
	jouer de la guitare électrique
	jouer du violon
	chanter

2 Read the texts and then complete the grid below with details of the four teenagers.

 Sophie — Mon ambition? Un jour, je veux être musicienne professionnelle. Mon talent, c'est jouer de la flûte.

 Lucas — Mon ambition? Un jour, je veux être chanteur professionnel. Mon talent, c'est chanter.

 **Olivier** — Mon talent, c'est jouer de la guitare. Un jour, je veux jouer dans un groupe de rock.

 Laura — Mon talent, c'est faire de la magie. Un jour, je veux être magicienne professionnelle.

Name	Talent	Wants to ...
Sophie	playing the _____	be a professional _____
Lucas		
Olivier		
Laura		

3 Change the underlined parts of the sentences below to write about your own talent and ambition.

Je m'appelle <u>Sophie</u>. J'ai <u>treize</u> ans. Mon talent, c'est <u>jouer de la flûte</u>. C'est <u>génial!</u> Un jour, je veux être <u>musicienne professionnelle</u>.

Studio 2 © Pearson Education Limited 2011

2 Je dois gagner! (pages 90–91)

 1 Give advice in French by unjumbling the sentences.
Then link each one to the matching English sentence.

1 toi. Tu confiance avoir dois en

Tu dois *avoir confiance en toi.*

2 jours. dois tous Tu les répéter

_____

3 aller Tu à dois l'audition.

_____

4 dois un Tu clip faire vidéo.

_____

5 Tu concours. dois au participer

_____

a You must take part in the competition.
b You must go to the audition.
c You must make a video clip.
d You must have confidence in yourself.
e You must practise every day.

 Two important verbs:
tu dois – you must
je peux – I can
je ne peux pas – I can't

2 Read the three notes and then say which person each of the symbols and phrases (1–7) belongs to.

Je ne peux pas participer au concours parce que je dois faire du babysitting. Désolé!

Sam

Je ne peux pas répéter chez moi ce soir parce que je dois faire mes devoirs. En plus, mes parents n'aiment pas le rock!

Alex

Je ne peux pas aller à l'audition parce que je dois faire un clip vidéo et je n'ai pas de caméra! Désolée!

Sandrine

Who ...?

1

_____

2

_____

3

_____

4 can't take part in a competition

_____

5 can't practise tonight

_____

6 can't go to the audition

_____

7 has parents who don't like rock

_____

1 The instructions haven't printed properly! Write them out correctly and then link each sentence to the correct picture.

1 Chante plus fort!

_____

2 Éteins ton portable!

_____

3 Enlève ton blouson!

_____

4 Jette ton chewing-gum!

_____

5 Regarde la caméra!

_____

6 N'oublie pas ta casquette!

_____

 **a**
 b
 **c**
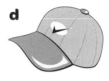 **d**
 e
 **f**

2 Read Sarah's letter and complete the English sentences below.

1 Sarah wants to be a

_____ .

2 Her _____ says no.

3 He says that _____ is more important.

4 He says that she has to do her

_____ .

5 Sarah says it's not

_____ .

> Chère Tante Isabelle,
>
> Mon problème: je veux être danseuse et je veux participer à un concours. Mais mon père dit 'non' parce que l'éducation est plus importante. Il dit que je dois faire mes devoirs. Ce n'est pas juste.
>
> Qu'est-ce que je peux faire?
>
> Sarah

3 Read Tante Isabelle's reply to Sarah's letter and find the French for the English phrases (1–8).

> Chère Sarah,
>
> Merci de ta lettre. Voici mes conseils:
> - Écoute ton père.
> - Fais plus d'efforts au collège.
> - Répète la danse tous les jours.
> - Puis redemande à ton père après un mois.
>
> Bonne chance!
>
> Tante Isabelle

1 thank you _____

2 my advice _____

3 listen _____

4 make _____

5 practise _____

6 every day _____

7 ask again _____

8 after a month _____

Les juges sont comment?

(pages 94–95)

1 Unjumble the letters to find eight adjectives. Put a ✓ next to them if they are positive and a ✗ if they are negative.

1	ucrle	_____
2	gntlie	_____
3	icèsner	_____
4	tupsdie	_____
5	mlipio	_____
6	ympsa	_____
7	arnramt	_____
8	aunvteix	_____

marrant	sincère
impoli	sympa
cruel	stupide
vaniteux	gentil

2 Read the descriptions of the four judges and complete the table with two words for each judge.

Olivia	Hugo	Kalim	Léa
kind			

Studio Grammaire

The adjective agrees with the person:

il est impatient → **elle** est impatient**e**

il est marrant → **elle** est marrant**e**

D'abord, Olivia. Oui, elle est assez gentille mais elle est aussi un peu sévère et très impatiente.

Puis Hugo. Oui, il est beau mais il est très arrogant et assez cruel.

Ensuite, Kalim. Kalim est sympa mais il est quelquefois un peu stupide et il est aussi assez vaniteux.

Enfin, Léa. Elle est intelligente et très belle. Elle est aussi assez marrante et elle est très sincère.

3 Write a similar description of this contestant. Adapt the passages above.

belle, intelligente, impolie

Karima

Karima est _____

_____

_____

_____

1 **Use a phrase from each cloud to translate the English sentences.**

1 I must continue my studies. _Je dois continuer mes études._
2 I want to work in Africa. _____
3 I'm going to sing on TV. _____
4 I would like to be rich. _____
5 I like playing the guitar. _____
6 I can be a professional singer. _____

> Je vais
> Je voudrais
> ~~Je dois~~
> Je peux
> Je veux
> J'aime

> être riche
> ~~continuer mes études~~
> jouer de la guitare
> travailler en Afrique
> être chanteur professionnel
> chanter à la télé

Studio Grammaire

Remember these important verbs:

j'aime	I like	je peux	I can
je veux	I want to	je voudrais	I'd like to
je dois	I must	je vais	I'm going to

2 **Complete the passage with the words in the box below.**

Une jeune musicienne

Moi, j'_____ jouer du
piano. Un jour, je _____
être musicienne professionnelle. Mais d'abord,
je dois continuer mes études au
_____ parce que
l'éducation est _____ .
Après, je vais _____ la musique
dans une école à _____ .

> importante adore Paris voudrais étudier collège

1 Spend three to four minutes reading the text and then write a few notes to describe what it is about.

- _____
- _____
- _____
- _____

- *Don't worry if you don't understand everything.*
- *Look for words which look like English and make a sensible guess.*
- *You will understand more when you have done the next few exercises.*

L'audition pour *Nouvelle Star*

Camille adore chanter, c'est son talent. Un jour, elle a surfé sur Internet et elle a trouvé des informations sur les auditions pour *Nouvelle Star*, une émission à la télé.

Aujourd'hui, c'est l'audition. Elle est devant trois juges!

Juge: Bonjour, et tu es …?

Camille: Bonjour! Je m'appelle Camille et j'habite à Nantes.

Juge: Quel est ton talent?

Camille: Mon talent, c'est chanter. C'est ma passion.

Juge: Et ton ambition?

Camille: Mon ambition? Un jour, je veux être chanteuse professionnelle.

Juge: Alors, enlève ton blouson, regarde la caméra et chante!

Camille: Mmm … ♪♪ *Héros* … ♪♪

2 Find the French for these phrases.

1 she surfed the internet _____
2 information about the auditions _____
3 a programme on TV _____
4 What's your talent? _____
5 It's my passion. _____
6 my ambition _____
7 One day, I want to be … _____
8 look at the camera _____

3 Read what the judge thought of Camille's singing. Below are eight phrases from the text – have a go at working out what they mean.

Juge: Bravo, bravo! C'était fantastique! Tu dois avoir confiance en toi. Tu as beaucoup de talent naturel. Tu es belle et intelligente et tu chantes très bien.

Camille: Merci, merci!

Juge: Alors, on vote; combien de «Oui»? Un … deux … trois. Trois «Oui», tu vas revenir pour l'audition finale!

Camille: Merci, merci, c'est fabuleux!

Juge: Alors, tu dois répéter tous les jours.

Camille: Oui, oui, merci! Au revoir!

> - Can you guess the meaning because it looks like an English word?
> - Look at where the word or phrase is in the text – does the rest of the sentence help?

1 Bravo! _Well done!_

2 talent naturel _____

3 tu chantes très bien _you …_____

4 on vote _____

5 tu vas revenir _you're going to …_____

6 l'audition finale _____

7 c'est fabuleux _it's …_____

8 tous les jours _every …_____

4 Are the sentences below true (✓) or false (✗)?

1 The judge did not think Camille was very good. ☐

2 He says she must have confidence in herself. ☐

3 He says she has lots of natural talent. ☐

4 He says she does not sing well. ☐

5 Camille gets two 'yes' votes. ☐

6 She is going to come back for the final audition. ☐

7 The judge says she has to practise every week. ☐

5 Write your own audition conversation. Use the one from page 48 and change a few details.

Juge: Bonjour, et tu es …?

(name): Bonjour! Je m'appelle _____ et j'habite à _____ .

Juge: Quel est ton talent?

(name): Mon talent, c'est _____ . C'est ma passion.

Les talents • *Talents*

Mon talent, c'est …	*My talent is …*
chanter	*singing*
danser	*dancing*
faire de la magie	*doing magic*
jouer du piano	*playing the piano*
jouer du violon	*playing the violin*
jouer de la guitare (électrique)	*playing the (electric) guitar*

Donner des conseils • *Giving advice*

Tu dois …	*You must …*
aller à l'audition	*go to the audition*
avoir confiance en toi	*have confidence in yourself*
faire un clip vidéo	*make a video clip*
participer au concours	*take part in the contest*
répéter tous les jours	*rehearse every day*

Les ambitions • *Ambitions*

Un jour, je veux être …	*One day, I want to be …*
chanteur professionnel/ chanteuse professionnelle	*a professional singer*
danseur professionnel/ danseuse professionnelle	*a professional dancer*
magicien professionnel/ magicienne professionnelle	*a professional magician*
professeur (de musique)	*a (music) teacher*
Je veux jouer …	*I want to play …*
dans un groupe de rock	*in a rock band*
dans un grand orchestre	*in a big orchestra*

Donner des excuses • *Making excuses*

Je ne peux pas parce que …	*I can't because …*
je dois faire mes devoirs	*I have to do my homework*
je dois faire du babysitting	*I have to do babysitting*
Je ne peux pas répéter chez moi.	*I can't rehearse at home.*
Tu peux …	*You can …*
faire tes devoirs demain	*do your homework tomorrow*
répéter chez moi	*rehearse at my place*

Vocabulaire

Donner des instructions • *Giving instructions*

Change ton attitude!	*Change your attitude!*
Chante plus fort!	*Sing louder!*
Enlève ton blouson!	*Take off your jacket!*
Éteins ton portable!	*Switch off your mobile!*
Fais plus d'efforts!	*Make more of an effort!*
Jette ton chewing-gum!	*Throw away your chewing-gum!*
Regarde la caméra!	*Look at the camera!*
N'oublie pas ta casquette!	*Don't forget your cap!*

Gagner • *Winning*

j'aime gagner	*I like winning*
je dois gagner	*I must win*
je peux gagner	*I can win*
je voudrais gagner	*I'd like to win*
je vais gagner	*I'm going to win*
je veux gagner	*I want to win*

Les mots essentiels • *High-frequency words*

à mon avis	*in my opinion*
trop	*too/too much*
je suis d'accord	*I agree*
je ne suis pas d'accord	*I disagree*
c'est	*it is*
d'accord	*OK*
pourquoi	*why*
pardon	*sorry/excuse me*

Le caractère • *Personality*

Il/Elle est ...	*He/She is ...*
très	*very*
trop	*too*
assez	*quite*
un peu	*a bit*
arrogant(e)	*arrogant*
beau/belle	*good-looking, beautiful*
cruel(le)	*cruel, nasty*
gentil(le)	*kind*
impatient(e)	*impatient*
impoli(e)	*rude*
intelligent(e)	*intelligent*
marrant(e)	*funny*
vaniteux/vaniteuse	*vain*
sévère	*strict, harsh*
sincère	*sincere, honest*
stupide	*stupid*
sympa	*nice*

Studio 2 © Pearson Education Limited 2011

1 **Record your steps for Module 5.**

2 **Look at the step descriptors on pages 62–63 and set your targets for Module 6.**

3 **Fill in what you need to do to achieve these targets.**

Listening	I have reached _____ Step in **Listening**.
	In Module 6, I want to reach _____ Step.
	I need to _____
	_____
	_____
	_____
Speaking	I have reached _____ Step in **Speaking**.
Salut!	In Module 6, I want to reach _____ Step.
	I need to _____
	_____
	_____
	_____
Reading	I have reached _____ Step in **Reading**.
	In Module 6, I want to reach _____ Step.
	I need to _____
	_____
	_____
	_____
Writing	I have reached _____ Step in **Writing**.
	In Module 6, I want to reach _____ Step.
	I need to _____
	_____
	_____
	_____

Studio Grammaire

Studio Grammaire

In Studio 2 you have met three tenses. In each tense the verb is different. You can also spot the tense from the time or frequency expression.

Tense	Verb	Time/Frequency expressions
Present tense One part to verb	*je regarde* *j'aime* *je vais*	*en général* (generally) *d'habitude* (usually) *en ce moment* (at the moment)
Past (perfect) tense Two parts to verb	*j'**ai** regard**é*** *j'**ai** aim**é*** *je **suis** all**é(e)***	*le weekend dernier* (last weekend) *samedi dernier* (last Saturday) *hier* (yesterday)
Future tense Two parts to verb	*je **vais** regard**er*** *je **vais** aim**er*** *je **vais** all**er***	*ce weekend* (this weekend) *samedi prochain* (next Saturday) *demain* (tomorrow)

Complete the crossword with the correct verbs from the box. Look at the time expression to decide which tense to use in each case.

1 Samedi dernier, je _____ au stade.

2 Hier, j'_____ au tennis.

3 En général, j'_____ ♡ les comédies.

4 En ce moment, j'_____ de la musique.

5 Le soir, je _____ des films d'action.

6 D'habitude, je _____ en ville le samedi.

7 Ce weekend, je _____ à la discothèque.

8 Le weekend dernier, j'_____ des souvenirs à Paris.

9 Samedi prochain, je _____ au foot.

10 Ce weekend, je _____ au restaurant.

11 Hier, j'_____ le Louvre à Paris.

12 Demain, je _____ au cinéma.

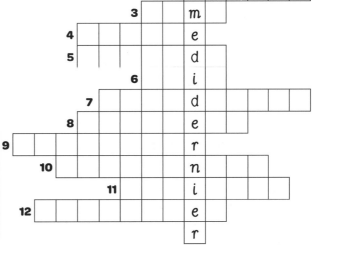

Present	**Past**	**Future**
vais	ai visité	vais jouer
écoute	ai acheté	vais danser
aime	suis allé	vais aller
regarde	ai joué	vais manger

Bonjour! Moi, je m'appelle Leila et j'ai quatorze ans. J'habite à Pointe-à-Pitre en Guadeloupe. Ici, on parle français.

J'habite dans un appartement avec ma mère et mon petit frère.

Ma passion, c'est le sport. Je joue au basket et au volley.

Voici des informations sur la Guadeloupe:

▶▶ Situation

- La Guadeloupe se trouve aux Antilles.
- En Guadeloupe, il y a huit îles.
- En Guadeloupe, on parle le français.

Amérique du Nord

Guadeloupe

Amérique du Sud

▶▶ Climat

- C'est un climat tropical.
- Quelquefois, il y a des cyclones.
- Il y a deux saisons: la saison humide (de juillet à novembre) et la saison sèche (de décembre à juin)

▶▶ Parc national de la Guadeloupe

- Dans le parc, il y a un volcan!
- Il y a aussi beaucoup de plantes et beaucoup d'animaux.

▶▶ Loisirs

- Il y a des plages fantastiques.
- On peut nager et faire du surf.

Don't worry if you don't understand everything.

- *Read through quickly first to see what you do understand.*
- *Use the headings and pictures to help you understand more.*
- *Look for words which look like English words.*

1 Read the text about Guadeloupe on page 54 and match up the French and English headings.

> Situation
> Loisirs
> Climat
> Parc national

> Climate
> National park
> Location
> Leisure activities

2 Read the introduction and complete the summary about Leila.

I'm called Leila and I'm _____ years old. I live in Pointe-à-Pitre
in _____ . Here we speak _____ .
I live in a _____ with my mum and little _____ .
My passion is _____ . I play _____ and
_____ .

3 Read the rest of the text about Guadeloupe and find the French for the English phrases (1–8).

1 eight islands _____
2 fantastic beaches _____
3 you can swim _____
4 a tropical climate _____
5 the wet season _____
6 the dry season _____
7 a volcano _____
8 a lot of plants _____

4 Match the information on French Polynesia in the box with the headings below.

Pays francophone: .... ☐
Situation: .... ☐

Langue officielle: .... ☐
Sports: .... ☐
....
Loisirs: .... ☐
....
Saison sèche: .... ☐
Saison humide: .... ☐

1 (de mai à octobre) Il fait beau.
2 (de novembre à avril) Il pleut beaucoup.
3 la Polynésie française
4 le français
5 du surf, du ski nautique, du jet-surf
6 dans l'océan Pacifique entre l'Australie et l'Amérique du Sud
7 On peut visiter des plages magnifiques.

1 **Read the article about healthy eating and then number the pictures below to match the sentences in the text.**

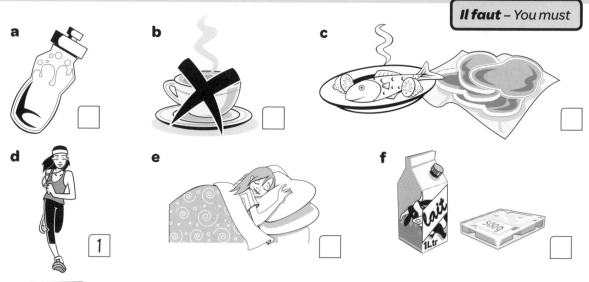

Voici des conseils pour les adolescents sportifs:

1 Il faut bien manger pour avoir assez d'énergie.
2 Il faut manger assez de glucides, par exemple des céréales et du pain.
3 Il faut prendre assez de calcium. On trouve du calcium dans le lait et le fromage.

4 Il faut prendre assez de protéines. On trouve des protéines dans le poisson et la viande.
5 Il faut boire de l'eau avant et après l'exercice.
6 Il faut éviter la caféine.
7 Il faut dormir au moins sept ou huit heures.

Il faut – *You must*

a ☐

b ☐

c ☐

d 1

e ☐

f ☐

g ☐

Look for words you do know in each sentence. Then try to work out the meaning of the rest of the sentence by finding words which look like English words.

2 **Read the tip box first! Then link the French expressions from the text (1–7) to the English (a–g).**

1 adolescents sportifs
2 assez de glucides
3 assez de calcium
4 assez de protéines
5 avant et après
6 éviter
7 dormir

a enough protein
b enough calcium
c before and after
d avoid
e sporty teenagers
f sleep
g enough carbohydrates

3 Look at the information about energy. Link the sentences below (1–6) to the correct group (a–f).

L'énergie

On mesure l'énergie en kilojoules. On a besoin d'énergie pour faire du sport. Mais combien d'énergie?

Qui a besoin de …

1 neuf mille kilojoules?
2 douze mille kilojoules?
3 seize mille kilojoules?
4 six mille kilojoules?
5 onze mille kilojoules?
6 dix mille kilojoules?

a adulte
b 11 ans
c 5 ans
d adulte actif
e 18 ans
f adulte très sportif

> **Qui a besoin de …?** – Who needs …?
> **mille** – 1,000

4 Read the passage about nutrition for footballers and fill in the gaps with the words in the box below.

Le régime alimentaire des footballeurs

Trois **1** _____ avant un match, il faut

2 _____ 200–300g de pommes de terre.

Il ne faut pas manger de **3** _____ à la bolognaise

ou de soupe à la **4** _____!

Après le match, il ne faut pas **5** _____ de bière.

Arsène Wenger, qui est entraîneur pour le **6** _____

d'Arsenal dit:

«Il faut manger du poisson, du poulet, beaucoup de

7 _____, et il faut boire

beaucoup d' **8** _____.

Il faut éviter le sucre, la viande rouge, les

9 _____ et les produits laitiers.»

> frites
> heures
> légumes
> manger
> spaghettis
> boire
> tomate
> club
> eau

Studio 2 © Pearson Education Limited 2011

1 Read the descriptions of two musicals relating to French history and find the French words and expressions for 1–10 below. (They are underlined in the text.)

Les Misérables, c'est <u>une comédie musicale</u> écrite en 1980. <u>Une adaptation anglaise</u> des *Mis* a commencé au Barbican à Londres en octobre 1985. C'est une comédie musicale <u>très populaire</u>. <u>Cinquante millions de spectateurs</u> ont vu *Les Mis* dans 38 pays et en 21 langues.

<u>L'histoire se passe</u> entre 1815 et 1832. Dans l'histoire, il y a une révolution des étudiants à Paris et on voit les barricades et les <u>batailles entre les révolutionnaires</u> et <u>l'armée française</u>.

La Révolution française est une autre comédie musicale écrite en 1973. C'est <u>le premier «opéra rock»</u> français.

L'action se passe pendant la Révolution française entre 1789 et 1794. C'est <u>une histoire d'amour</u> entre Charles Gauthier et une jeune aristocrate, Isabelle de Montmoreau. Pendant la comédie musicale, on voit <u>les évènements de la Révolution</u>.

1 the French army
2 a love story
3 a musical comedy
4 the events of the Revolution
5 fifty million spectators
6 battles between the revolutionaries
7 an English adaptation
8 the first rock opera
9 very popular
10 the story takes place

2 Read the text again and match up the numbers with the phrases they relate to.

a 1980
b 1985
c 50 million
d 38
e 21
f 1815–1832
g 1973
h 1789–1794

1 the number of countries in which *Les Mis* has been staged
2 the years during which the story of *Les Mis* takes place
3 the number of languages *Les Mis* has been translated into
4 the year *Les Mis* was written
5 the year *La Révolution française* was written
6 the years during which the action of *La Révolution française* takes place
7 the year *Les Mis* opened in London
8 the number of people who have seen *Les Mis*

3 Read the passage and note whether the sentences below are true (✓) or false (✗).

Ma passion, c'est le théâtre musical.

Ma passion, c'est le théâtre musical.

J'adore chanter et danser. Un jour, je veux être chanteur professionnel au théâtre.

J'adore aussi regarder des spectacles. Mon spectacle préféré, c'est *Les Misérables*.

Le weekend dernier, je suis allé à Paris avec <u>ma mère</u> et j'ai vu *Les Misérables* au théâtre. On a voyagé en <u>train</u>.

Avant le spectacle, j'ai visité <u>la tour Eiffel</u>, puis je suis arrivé au théâtre à <u>huit heures du soir</u>.

J'ai adoré la musique!

Après le spectacle, je suis allé <u>au restaurant</u> et j'ai mangé <u>une pizza</u>. C'était délicieux.

Ce weekend, je vais retourner à Paris et je vais voir *La Révolution française*. Super!

Thomas

1 Thomas's passion is classical music. ☐

2 He wants to be a professional singer. ☐

3 His favourite show is *La Révolution française*. ☐

4 He went to Paris with his mum last weekend. ☐

5 They travelled by train. ☐

6 They visited the Eiffel Tower after the show. ☐

7 They arrived at the theatre at 8 p.m. ☐

8 After the show, they went to a restaurant. ☐

9 Thomas did not like his food very much. ☐

10 Next weekend he's going to stay at home. ☐

4 Write your own account of a musical that you have seen recently. Change the details that are underlined in the text.

Record your steps for Module 6.

Listening	I have reached _____ Step in **Listening**.
Speaking	I have reached _____ Step in **Speaking**.
Reading	I have reached _____ Step in **Reading**.
Writing	I have reached _____ Step in **Writing**.

Look back through your workbook and note down the step you achieved in each skill by the end of each Module.

	Listening	Speaking	Reading	Writing
1 T'es branché(e)?				
2 Paris, je t'adore!				
3 Mon identité				
4 Chez moi, chez toi				
5 Quel talent?!				
6 Studio découverte				

You now have a record of your progress in French for the whole year.

Attainment Target 1:

Listening and responding

1st Step	I can understand some familiar spoken words and phrases.
2nd Step	I can understand a range of familiar spoken phrases and opinions.
3rd Step	I can understand the main points and opinions from short spoken passages using familiar words and phrases
4th Step	I can understand the main points and opinions from spoken passages and some of the detail. I can recognise if people are speaking about the future **OR** the present.
5th Step	I can understand opinions, details and reasons in spoken passages. I can recognise if people are speaking about the future **OR** the past as well as the present.

Attainment Target 2:

Speaking

Salut!

1st Step	I can say single words and short phrases.
2nd Step	I can answer simple questions and give basic information and opinions using familiar words.
3rd Step	I can ask and answer simple questions with opinions. Take part in brief conversations.
4th Step	I can take part in simple conversations speaking about the present or future. Give my opinions with simple reasons. Start to speak spontaneously (e.g. give my opinion without being asked).
5th Step	I can take part in simple conversations on a range of topics. Describe, give information and express my opinions with reasons. Speak spontaneously (e.g. ask unexpected questions). Speak about the future OR the past as well as the present.

Attainment Target 3:

Reading and responding

1st Step	I can understand familiar words and phrases. Read them aloud.
2nd Step	I can understand familiar phrases and opinions. Read them aloud.
3rd Step	I can understand the main points and opinions in short written texts using familiar words.
4th Step	I can understand the main points, opinions and some detail in short texts (including simple poems and songs). Use a bilingual dictionary or glossary to look up unfamiliar words. Recognise if the texts are about the future or the present.
5th Step	I can understand the main points, opinions and detail in a range of shorter and longer texts (including poems and songs). Recognise if the texts are about the future **OR** the past as well as the present.

Attainment Target 4:

Writing

1st Step	I can write or copy single words correctly.
2nd Step	I can write a few short sentences following a model. Write some familiar words from memory.
3rd Step	I can write several sentences with help, giving information and simple opinions.
4th Step	I can write short texts using language from memory and giving opinions and simple reasons. Write about the present or the future.
5th Step	I can write short texts giving and asking for information, opinions and reasons. Write about the future **OR** the past as well as the present.

Heinemann is part of

PEARSON

T 0845 630 33 33
F 0845 630 77 77
customer.orders@pearson.com
www.pearsonschools.co.uk

ISBN 978-0-435-03013-1